I ♥ CUTE UNICORNS

Buster Books

Illustrated by
Amanda Hillier,
Lizzie Preston and
Angelika Scudamore

Edited by Emma Taylor
Designed by Derrian Bradder

First published in Great Britain in 2020 by Buster Books,
an imprint of Michael O'Mara Books Limited, 9 Lion Yard,
Tremadoc Road, London SW4 7NQ

W www.mombooks.com/buster   f Buster Books   🐦 @BusterBooks

ISBN: 978-1-78055-678-9

2 4 6 8 10 9 7 5 3 1

This book was printed in January 2020 by
Shenzhen Wing King Tong Paper Products Co. Ltd.,
Shenzhen, Guangdong, China.

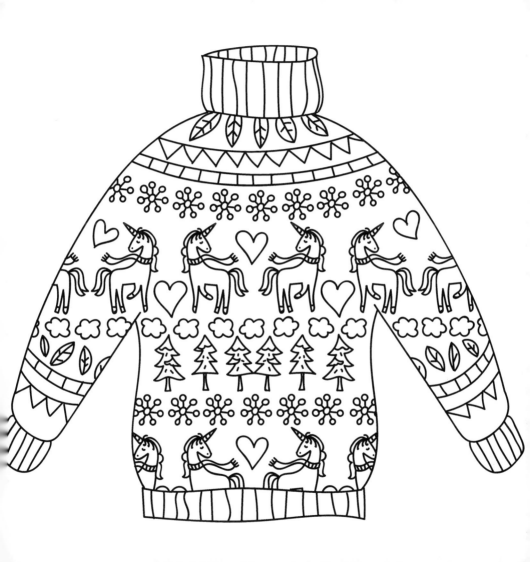